HOMEBODIES

BY

CHARLES ADDAMS

SIMON AND SCHUSTER · NEW YORK · 1954

THIRD PRINTING
LIBRARY OF CONGRESS CATALOG CARD NUMBER: 54-9805
DEWEY DECIMAL CLASSIFICATION NUMBER: 741.5
MANUFACTURED IN THE UNITED STATES OF AMERICA
PRINTED BY MURRAY PRINTING COMPANY, WAKEFIELD, MASS.
BOUND BY AMERICAN BOOK-STRATFORD PRESS, INC., NEW YORK

HOMEBODIES

"Nothing much, Agnes. What's new with you?"

"Now, remember—act casual."

"*Mr. Mitchell! You __know__ you don't have kitchen privileges.*"

"Sanders speaking. Stop all production on XP15, recall all shipments, wire every doctor in the country, and _hurry_!"

"All right, children, a nice big sneer, now."

"I'm sorry, sonny. We've run out of candy."

"There's an amusing little legend connected with it—something about a
dreadful curse."

"*Now don't tell me you had anthropologist for lunch.*"

"You forgot the eye of newt."

"I should think Alice would at least be on hand to help you move."

"It's *priceless*. Normie's building a rocket to shoot Pamela to the moon."

"*And this is your Uncle Cosimo, a man of whom it may be truly said he left the world a little worse for his having lived in it.*"

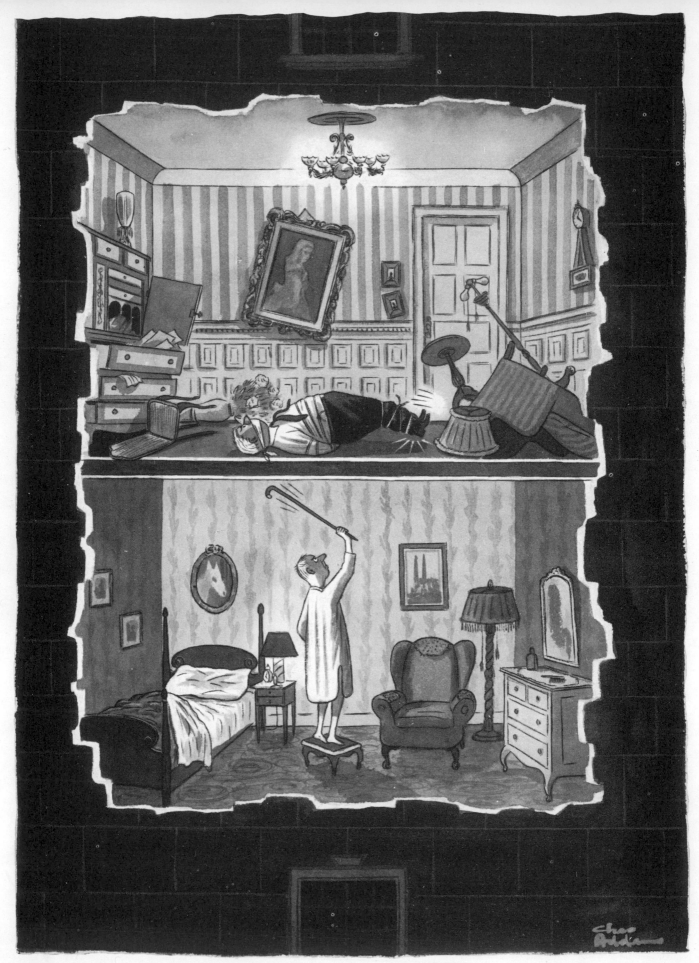

"One thing I'll say for him—he's always been a good provider."

FOR SALE
LOT APPROX. 400' X 600'
INQUIRE
WITHIN

"What light you giving it?"

"Would you care to step in here and see how it looks in the dark?"

"*You've never felt that way about me.*"

"The little dears! They still believe in Santa Claus."

"Excuse me, sir, but are you the Arthur Johnson who lost this diary?"

"*You're going to shoot a hundred and fourteen, dear.*"

"*Well, I don't see any point in looking any farther. It was probably just one of those wild rumors.*"

"Just the kind of day that makes you feel good to be alive!"

"*I like them. They _wear_ well.*"

"*For heaven's sake, Ed, holler something besides 'help'. People might think we're really in trouble.*"

"*Something in sneakers?*"

"Delmonico's—and hurry!"

"... then good old Scrooge, bless his heart, turned to Bob Cratchit and snarled, 'Let me hear another sound from <u>you</u> and you'll keep Christmas by losing your <u>situation</u>.'"

"Death ray, fiddlesticks! Why it doesn't even slow them up."

"It's very interesting, but I'm afraid we only publish science _fiction_."

"*Go right ahead, Pomfret. The entries closed two weeks ago.*"

"*Everything happens to me.*"

"I give up, Robert. What does have two horns, one eye, and creeps?"

"Then the dragon gobbled up the handsome young prince and his lovely
bride and lived happily ever after."

"Oh, for goodness' sake, forget it, Beasley. Play another one."

" Well, good night, Ahmed. If you need anything, just rub."

"And now we present 'Mary and Bill,' the story of a family that might be
your next-door neighbors, and of their everyday life among everyday people
just like yourselves..."

"Wouldn't you know that at a time like this Haley would be off somewhere photographing some damn ritual?"

"*Mom, can I have the broom tonight?*"

"*I have a question from a lady in Astoria. She wants to know the best method of removing bloodstains from a broadloom rug.*"

"*Have you got a minute, Dr. Headley? We think we may have found a new carnivorous specimen.*"

"All right, now, a little smile."